POETIC TREASURES

BATH

Edited by Rachael Radford

FOREWORD

This year, the Young Writers' Hidden Treasures competition proudly presents a showcase of the best poetic talent from over 72,000 up-and-coming writers nationwide.

Young Writers was established in 1991 and we are still successful, even in today's technologically-led world, in promoting and encouraging the reading and writing of poetry.

The thought, effort, imagination and hard work put into each poem impressed us all, and once again, the task of selecting poems was a difficult one, but nevertheless, an enjoyable experience.

We hope you are as pleased as we are with the final selection and that you and your family continue to be entertained with *Hidden Treasures Bath* for many years to come.

CONTENTS

Matthew Strange	17
Thomas Drake	17
Rebecca Jones	18
Jordan Short	18
Natalie Webb	19
Sophie Burman	19
Jake Ball	20
Joe Wallis-Poulton	20
Aimee Samways	21
Alice Norris	21
Elise Burvill	22
Gino Gibilaro	22
Kieran Cox	23
Claire Kingwell	23
Nicola Woodland	24
Louise Payton	24
Andrew Strange	24
Tanya Murphy-Hennessey	25
Peter Keeling	25
George Smith	25
Jamie-Lee Rodaway	26
Sophie Caldwell	26
David Locke	27
Stephen Ralph	27
Natasha Harris	28
Sophie Drake	28
Alex Hussey	28
Tom Fry	29
Katie Durbin	29
Seb Burvill	29
Craig Wall	30
Linda Liang Hu	30
Cema Rahim	31
William Robinson	31
Jessica Ball	32
Luca Elice	32
Hannah Latchem	33
Lisa Ghosn	33

Frankie Stratton	76
Rhianne Bolton	76
Daniel Keevill	76
Sylvia Bevan	77
John Partridge	77
Manon Le Garnec	77
Jessica Warlow	78
Ryan Farrell	78
Victoria Dent	79
Rosie Dunn	80
Maria Wong	80
Jack Chalmers	80
Rachel Prest	81
Anna Piercy	81
Joseph Roberts	81
Patrick Crook	82
Victoria Cummings	82
Joseph Marchant	82
Anthony McLaughlin	83
George Cox	83
Eleanor Parker	83
Bethanie Locke	84
Samuel Sherry	84
Joel Bassett	85
James Creese	86
Maisie McEvoy	86
Jack Davies	86
Rowland Goodbody	87
Joshua Carey	87
Andrew Eades	87
Bruce Coram	88
Alice Piekarski	88
Sam Kelson	89
Douglas Kelly	89
Oliver Hawthorne	89
Brenden King	90
Elizabeth Tyler	90

St Mary's RC Primary School

Michael Brennan	90
Joshua Angell	91
Grace Byron	91
Adam Copus	91
Alexander Jacobs	92
Sam Belizaire	92
Gemma Tugwell	92
Keely Noad	93
Rebecca Costello	93
Christina Bovill-Rose	94
Drew Goodchild	94

Weston All Saints Primary School

Joseph Scarff	94
Emily Hurford	95
Bethany Walker	95
Imogen Tinkler	96
Michael Hiscott	96
Samuel Taylor	97
Sam White	98
Juliet Carrick	98
Joshua White	99
Alex Bryant	100
Amy Cousins	100
Amy Rotheram	101
Maisie Coyle	101
Natasha Jacobs	102
Tom Folkes	102
Oliver Soar	103
Paolo Hollis	103
Corinne Plank	104
Sophie Burton	104
Rio Arthur	105
Hannah Kennedy	106

The Poems

THE TRAPPED BIRD

Down in the wood,
In one of the tall trees,
There is a feather nest,
Which is blowing in the breeze.

And way up there,
In that spot out of sight,
There is a little bird,
Struggling with all his might.

For he is caught,
In an evil bird's lair,
There's only one way out,
But that way's through the air.

The problem is,
That this bird cannot fly,
It has an injured wing,
So if it tries it will die.

I climb the tree,
To save the helpless bird,
I reach the hidden nest,
Then an awful cry is heard.

It's the jackdaw,
Closing in on its prey,
But it's the bird it wants,
So I scare it away.

The bird is safe,
It has come home with me,
Its wing is on the mend,
So soon it will be free.

Sarah Raby (11)
Monkton Combe Junior School

HIDDEN TREASURES

I was sitting alone on a rock by the sea,
When I heard a voice singing to me.
I stood up, responded with my head held high,
But nothing answered except a strangled cry.

It could have been my echo but I was sure it was not,
Someone is in trouble I thought, an evil plot.
So picking up my bag, I felt my way,
But soon enough I stopped that, I'd be there all day!

Suddenly I spotted a bottle in the sand,
A note was inside written by strange hand.
Then I realised it was no ordinary flask,
The note inside showed an extraordinary task!

Then seeing a ripple and hearing a splash,
And, 'Tonight we'll have some mermaid mash!'
Suddenly I heard a 'Ho, ho, ho and a bottle of rum,'
And realised it was time to run.

As I sprinted from that place,
I saw a pirate with a mangled face,
Then I saw he held a large gun,
He could pull the trigger and the job would be done.

When I got home all in a sweat,
Gran said, 'Dear, are you upset?'
'No, no, no, I'm fine,' I lied,
Don't be stupid, you nearly died.

On the sofa, as I ate some chocolates,
I told Gran all about the ugly pirate
And how he guarded his gold at great measure.
'Aha,' said Gran, 'the hidden treasure.'

I don't know how she knew,
But to her this story wasn't new!

Iona Napier (11)
Monkton Combe Junior School

MY DOUBLE BASS

My double bass is deep and grand,
Sitting on its stand looking beautiful and proud.
My bass and I have a lot of fun,
But sometimes we sound like a rusty old gate.

It's so big for just an eighth,
Taller than me it is.
People think it's only a cello,
I always end up explaining what it is.

The tuning pegs are glistening gold,
The head is proficiently carved.
They made it have that lovely spiral,
Which attracts all who would come near.

The bass' spike is like a soldier's spear,
Punching the heart of the carpet.
My bass' back has a perfect curve,
But I have to sit up straight to play.

My double bass is deep and grand,
Sitting on its stand looking beautiful and proud.
My bass and I have a lot of fun,
And we'll always belong together.

Jamie Bateman (9)
Monkton Combe Junior School

OH, WHAT A CHORE

It was all going well,
When one day at tea,
Mum stood up,
And said to Dad and me:

'I'm having a baby.'
Dad shrieked out,
Then fell off his chair,
And I jumped up, then gave a shout.

A few weeks later Mum got a bump,
And everyone knew what was happening,
She got bigger and bigger and bigger each day,
Until one day there was a ping.

Dad and me were running around,
Looking out for Mum,
I got the phone and dialled 999,
Then waited for the ambulance to come.

Mum went off and Dad and me followed,
Very nervously,
When we got there,
Dad went with Mum and I had a cup of tea.

When it was over, I went in,
There wasn't one baby or two or three, but four.
They were all crying with their mouths opened wide,
And I thought, oh what a chore!

Jessica Helyar (10)
Monkton Combe Junior School

COLOURS

What is red? A rose is red
In the flower bed.

What is blue? The sea is blue
Where the whales glide through.

What is green? The seaweed is green
In a beautiful scene.

What is yellow? A buttercup is yellow
He's a pretty little fellow.

What is white? The snow is white
In the daylight.

What is pink? A pig is pink
That sits on the brink.

What is colourful?
    A rainbow is colourful.

Jade Biggs (8)
Oldfield Park Junior School

MY TEDDY

Big cuddler
Ribbon wearer
Some bigger
Some smaller
Fur bearer
Some chubbier
Bad sharer
Good carer.

Amy Drake (10)
Oldfield Park Junior School

WHALES AND DOLPHINS

Look at them,
Dancing in the water,
They look like dancers,
Dancing in the deep sea.

Swallowing fish
And swimming along the way.
Oh, look! He's waving at me.

Different colours, black and blue,
Whatever the colour, they swim in the sea.
The opposite of flying like a bumblebee.

They are jumping with happiness
And the jump in a ring,
They swim in beauty, like they're a king.

David Kenward (8)
Oldfield Park Junior School

JUNGLE

Look at that,
All those trees, monkeys, birds looking at me.
Let's go and see what we can find,
Maybe some treasure, or eve n a mine.
I'm halfway in, taking little, little steps,
Being so careful for the jungle kept.
All the people who know the secrets of the jungle,
Maybe I'll know if I don't go so slow.

And now I know.

George Haughton (8)
Oldfield Park Junior School

THE BOGGIE MONSTER

I looked up at the clock
and saw it was seven o'clock.
I yawned and rubbed my eyes.

I am only little so I have to go to bed.
I brushed my teeth
and went upstairs.

I tried to get to sleep
but something was bothering me!
It was music.

It was coming from under my bed
and it was spooky music.
I moved all my junk and saw a spinning whirlpool.

I got sucked in
and saw the most scary thing in the world . . .
The boggie monster!

Lucy Garbutt (10)
Oldfield Park Junior School

CAT

Henry and Harry licking at my toys
Henry is purring at my bed
At my sister's house I play with them
They always scratch my sister
She goes 'Ouch! That hurt!'
They always play a game called cat fight
They run around the house and jump up on each other
Silly cats!

Thomas Burles (10)
Oldfield Park Junior School

WHAT IS RED?

What is red? My top is red
Lying on my bed.
What is black? My dad's hat is black
On top of his back pack.
What is white? Paper is white
In my sight.
What is pink? The sunset is pink
Don't stare or blink.
What is blue? The sea is blue
So is the sky too.

Zoe Macey (8)
Oldfield Park Junior School

TEDDIES

T   eddies are cuddly, teddies are sweet
E   veryone loves teddies, especially me
D   otted teddies, spotted teddies, furry teddies, fluffy teddies
D   ogs scare teddies, that is why I don't have one
I   t is very nice to smooth a teddy
E   asy to cuddle, they love to cuddle
S   ometimes they sleep in your bed to keep you warm.

Laura Weston (9)
Oldfield Park Junior School

SUN HAIKU

Very, very hot,
A lot bigger than the Earth,
Its core is hotter.

Finn Shields (7)
Oldfield Park Junior School

WHAT IS RED?

What is red? A rose is red
Lying in its flower bed.

What is blue? The sea is blue
Where the sharks swim through.

What is green? A wood is green
What a beautiful scene.

What is yellow? A sunflower is yellow
What a beautiful fellow.

Katie Minchin (9)
Oldfield Park Junior School

CATS

Cats are furry, cats are purry,
Cats are sneaky, cats are sneezy,
Cats are sleepy, cats are scratchy,
Cats are pouncy, cats are playful,
Cats are eating, cats are drinking.

Amber Hitchcock (10)
Oldfield Park Junior School

SUN HAIKU

Just a hot fireball,
Falling from the lovely, bright sky,
What a boiling day!

Jack Stead (7)
Oldfield Park Junior School

WHAT IS RED?

What is red? A rose is red,
Sunbathing in its flower bed.

What is blue? The sky is blue,
Where the birds fly through.

What is green? The grass is green,
With the bugs between.

What is yellow? A buttercup is yellow,
What a pretty little fellow.

What is white? The snow is white,
When I get in a snow fight!
  What is black?

Jessica Newman (8)
Oldfield Park Junior School

WHAT IS WHITE?

What is white? The clouds are white,
Sailing through the light.
What is red? A rose is red,
In its little bed.
What is yellow? A buttercup is yellow,
He's a jolly fellow.
What is blue? The sea is blue,
Where the fish swim through.
What is green? The grass is green,
With buttercups between.

Aaron Baker (8)
Oldfield Park Junior School

I LOVE SUMMER

On the beach licking ice creams,
On sports day getting in teams,
On Friday going to drama,
In the garden eating banana,
In the park on the slide,
At the funfair on a ride,
In the sun sunbathing,
Having a party, eating jelly,
Yippee! We're going to Disneyland,
On the beach playing with sand,
Next week it's school,
In PE we will be playing ball,
Whoo! It's really hot,
In the park playing ball,
In the meadow with the flowers,
On holiday in London with the really tall towers.

Chloé Chandler (8)
Oldfield Park Junior School

BLUE

What is blue? My bedroom is blue, it's so new.
What is blue? The wavy sea is blue.
What is blue? The bluebells are blue in their cosy little bed.
What is blue? The sky is blue.
What is blue? My uniform is blue.
What is blue? My dress is blue.
What is blue? My eyes are blue.
What is blue? My car is blue.

Miriam Breakah (8)
Oldfield Park Junior School

WHAT IS BLACK?

What is black? The night is black
When the stars twinkle.
What is black? My school shoes are black
When I go to school.
What is black? My hair is black
When it blows in the air.
What is black? My dress is black
When I go to a party.
What is black? My cat is black
When it sits on a doormat.
What is black? My favourite colour is black.

Emily Whittock (8)
Oldfield Park Junior School

THROUGH MY WINDOW

I look through my window and there I see
daffodils staring at me.
Most are yellow but some are faded white
and I say to myself, 'What a beautiful sight.'

Katy Phillips (8)
Oldfield Park Junior School

SNOW HAIKU

No food for the birds,
In the falling winter storm,
Just like a blanket.

Serena Wall (8)
Oldfield Park Junior School

IN THE DARK

In the dark I had a fright,
It sounded like something just took flight,
It echoed around in the night,
Whilst the moon looked shiny bright,
I thought it was a ghost,
That's what I thought it was the most,
I told the story at school to boast,
But really it scared me the most!

Anthony Jack (10)
Oldfield Park Junior School

ROCKY THE DOLPHIN

I was sitting in a boat on the calm sea,
A dolphin came along,
I called it Rocky.
I put a tag on him
So I would know where he was in the sea.
Rocky the dolphin was in danger,
So I took him home with me!

Joshua Cox (9)
Oldfield Park Junior School

SNOW HAIKU

Just snow falling down
Falling down without a sound
Settles like icing.

Jade Anderson (8)
Oldfield Park Junior School

BONFIRE NIGHT

Be safe tonight
The fireworks are glowing, swirling and circling
Boom
Bang
Smiling at them, you like the cool sound
Fire hot with a man on top
Loud and scary, dogs bark
Birds fly away and cats say 'Miaow'
This is fantastic, sizzling and lots of noises
People's eyes glowing with lots of colours
Red, green, yellow, gold and lots more too
Remember, remember, the 5th of November.

Rebecca Land (8)
Oldfield Park Junior School

WHAT IS RED?

What is red?
A rose is red, growing in a flower bed.

What is blue?
My jeans are blue that I wear at the weekend.

What is green?
The grass is green, flowing to one side in the wind.

What is black?
The night sky is black when I go to sleep.

What is white?
The clouds are white flying in the sky like birds.

Emily Doman (8)
Oldfield Park Junior School

BEDTIME

Oh no, it's half-past nine,
It is bedtime,
It is the worst time of the day,
Because we cannot play.
It is also scary,
Because I am scared of things that are hairy,
Like monsters and spiders and an alien snake
And things that make me get a headache.
But the worst thing of them all,
Is that weird thing on the wall,
It gives me an awful fright
And stops me from turning on the light.
It only comes out at night.

Jadon Williams (10)
Oldfield Park Junior School

MY FAMILY

Jim and Hayley,
Have had a baby.

He's called Jake
And he's never awake.

My mum's in her forties,
My dad's in his thirties.

I am me,
Just plain, old me.

Victoria Farnham (8)
Oldfield Park Junior School

SCARED OF THE DARK!

My mum says goodnight,
She says, 'Mind the bed bugs don't bite.'

Will they bite me, eat me up?
Will they bash me with a cup?

Or will they stay where they've been put?
There's a monster up my chimney and he's called Soot.

Rachel Eades (9)
Oldfield Park Junior School

JANUARY

J   anuary is my favourite month,
A   nd you may be able to guess why!
N   obody in my house is allowed to forget,
U   nderstand that there is a day that is very special to me.
A   nd it's my birthday!
R   emember it,
Y   ou better had!

Lauren Orchard (10)
Oldfield Park Junior School

ONE HUNGRY DINOSAUR

It roars, it frowns, it stamps really hard,
It can reach the clouds and it can reach the floor.
It can eat its dinner really fast, faster than a giant.
That's one hungry dinosaur.

Nathan Simmonds (9)
Oldfield Park Junior School

RACING CAR

Revving engines waiting to go, there's the green light
And they're off, number 3 is in the lead
Closely chased by number 1.
Into the pits, as quickly as possible,
Now coming out, cars passing as quick as a flash
Giving chase, what a race!

Coming round the corner at tremendous speed
And there's a crash, number 1 right off the track,
Flames are bursting out,
Racing to the finish line, yeah, I've won!

Matthew Strange (10)
Oldfield Park Junior School

MY TIME LINE

When I was 1 I sucked my thumb,
When I was 2 I said 'Boo!'
When I was 3 I bumped my knee
When I was 4 I shut the door
When I was 5 I did a fantastic dive
When I was 6 I picked up sticks
When I was 7 I went to Devon
When I was 8 I sat and ate
When I was 9 I did a rhyme
When I was 10 I did it again!

Thomas Drake (10)
Oldfield Park Junior School

LIFE

Life is a special gift
From someone very special,
Life can be fun
If you aren't bad,
Life is a treasure
So remember that!
Life is more than money
It's at the top! It's the best!
Life to criminals
Is a disaster!
Life
Is really real,
Life is joyful
It's more than you think!
Life is what you have
Like everyone else.

Rebecca Jones (11)
Oldfield Park Junior School

SLOW-WORMS

S low-worms are not slow,
L onely, they cry,
O n a summer day they lie out on top of their nest,
W hen it is winter they hibernate.

W et slow-worms slither faster,
O n a wet day they go down to the bottom of the compost,
R ight down in the dark,
M ums don't like them, but children do,
S lithery slow-worms, secretly sleeping.

Jordan Short (9)
Oldfield Park Junior School

I WENT TO THE ZOO

I went to the zoo,
I said to my friend
she could come too.
I asked my mum
if she could come too.
She said, 'Yes,'
we both shouted, 'Yes.'
My mum is the best,
better than all the rest.
When we got to the zoo
we had a great time,
there was loads to do.

Natalie Webb (9)
Oldfield Park Junior School

RAIN

The rain falling
Splish, splash, splish, splash,
Rain making puddles,
Puddles getting bigger and bigger,
Rain again hammering on the floor,
The rain getting louder and louder,
Rain knocking against the window,
People moaning that they can't go out,
The rain dripping down the window,
At last the rain has stopped!

Hooray!

Sophie Burman (9)
Oldfield Park Junior School

MY LIFE

When I was 0 I cried,
When I was 1 I had my first birthday,
When I was 2 I could walk,
When I was 3 I could talk,
When I was 4 I fell in the thorns,
When I was 5 I went to school
When I was 6 I could eat
When I was 7 I could climb,
When I was 8 I had a friend over called Steven,
When I was 9 I had a McDonald's for my birthday.

Jake Ball (9)
Oldfield Park Junior School

MY CAT

Food eater
Curtain climber
Lazy sleeper
Water drinker
Fast runner
Good jumper
Play fighter
Mouse chaser
Tail chaser
Treat scoffer
Sofa clawer
Loud purrer.

Joe Wallis-Poulton (10)
Oldfield Park Junior School

SOMETHING MISSING

I'm sure I've forgotten something
It's not my teddy bear, it's on the bed,
Or my books, they're in my room,
I'm very late for school,
It's not my ruler, it's in my school bag,
Or my pencil case, it's ready to go,
It's not my pen, it's very safe,
It's not my dish, it's in the dishwasher,
It's not to find my hairbrush, it's found,
It's got to be something,
Oh, oh, it's my lunch box,
I'd better ask Mum, I hope she knows where it is.
'It's in your school bag, love,' she replies.
Oh, I have to go to school!

Aimee Samways (11)
Oldfield Park Junior School

FLOWERS

Colourful wearer
Good smeller
Bee catcher
Good grower
Water lover
Slug hater
Food maker
Sun bather
Root hider.

Alice Norris (10)
Oldfield Park Junior School

NERVOUS

Becky was nervous, it was her first day at school.
She got out of the car, she suddenly froze;
Her feet were glued to the spot.
Her hands were like rocks in her pockets.
She stumbled forward, with legs like jelly.
She had butterflies flying around in her stomach.
She felt sick.
Becky slowly walked into the playground,
A lady said, 'Hello!'
She tried to say hello back but her throat was dry.
Her mind went blank.
She started shaking like a leaf.
She went as white as a sheet.
She had cold sweat pouring down her face.
Her palms were all clammy.
School's over, what a relief!

Elise Burvill (11)
Oldfield Park Junior School

SNAKES

They're in the grass,
They're in the desert and they're ready to fight,
You can have them as pets,
But they might give you a fright,
They slither and hiss,
But the strange thing is, they have no knee,
They are really cool to me.
        Snakes!

Gino Gibilaro (9)
Oldfield Park Junior School

WHAT IS RED?

What is red?
A fire is red, burning hot.

What is green?
The grass is green, growing all the time.

What is blue?
My spelling book is blue, being written in all the time.

What is brown?
Wood is brown, growing splintery all the time.

What is yellow?
The sun is yellow, burning flames.

What is black?
My shoes are black, getting worn out.

What is white?
My freezer is white, freezing cold.

What is pink?
My skin is pink, growing freckles.

Kieran Cox (8)
Oldfield Park Junior School

AUTUMN

It's getting colder,
leaves are falling off the trees.
It's very foggy.

Claire Kingwell (9)
Oldfield Park Junior School

Rain

I'm dripping wet as I walk through the pouring rain,
It feels as if I'm in a swimming pool.
My umbrella's soaking wet, it's dripping off the edge,
Plip, plop, drip, drop!
People stamping in the puddles making themselves wet,
Cars whizzing along the road splashing in puddles,
Hooray! At last the rain has come to a stop.

Nicola Woodland (9)
Oldfield Park Junior School

The Monster Under My Bed

I think there's a monster under my bed,
With big sharp teeth and yellow claws.
I think there's a monster under my bed,
Who has big beady eyes and is slimy too.
I am going to be brave and look under my bed,
Relief, it's only my toys!

Louise Payton (9)
Oldfield Park Junior School

What Is Blue?

Blue is the colour of the bright sky,
Blue is the colour of the sparkling water,
Blue is the colour of my super fast bike,
Blue is the colour of our school jumper,
Blue is the colour of my Umbro pencil,
My favourite colour is blue.

Andrew Strange (8)
Oldfield Park Junior School

Rain

Dripping wet I walk through the rain, splashing,
making puddles everywhere, in boots and coats.
I wear an umbrella over my head keeping me dry,
little children are screaming and shouting,
crying and stamping in puddles.
Suddenly the rain comes to a stop.
I put down my umbrella and walk home.

Tanya Murphy-Hennessey (9)
Oldfield Park Junior School

War

Shells falling,
Bombs dropping,
Bullets flying,
Tanks rolling,
Guns firing,
Rifles shooting,
And all I've got is a steel helmet.

Peter Keeling (9)
Oldfield Park Junior School

A Big Wish

I wish I could dance,
I wish I could sing,
I wish I could prance,
I wish I could bring
Happiness to everyone.

George Smith (9)
Oldfield Park Junior School

CANDY LAND

Sweets, sweets everywhere,
Chocolate is in my hair.
Three times you've got to hop,
If you want my lollipop.
Sherbet's really fizzy,
Sometimes it'll make you dizzy.
Mars bars, I'll have seven,
When I eat them I'm in Heaven,
Rolos, they melt so fast,
Eat them quickly or they won't last.
Smarties are different colours,
I'm not gonna give them to my mother.
Loads of sweets in my mouth,
They're all gonna stay in my house.

Jamie-Lee Rodaway (10)
Oldfield Park Junior School

MUM

Bedroom tidier,
Toy finder,
Big thinker,
Non drinker,
Good reader,
Bad sleeper,
Washing doer,
Food maker,
Dirt hater,
Animal lover.

Sophie Caldwell (10)
Oldfield Park Junior School

FERRARI AND PORSCHE

Ferrari

F ast as sound,
E ngine roaring
R ound the track at 200 mph,
R amming the barrier on every corner,
A t the pit stop they make repairs.
R efilling the fuel tanks.
I t's time to race again . . .

Porsche

P ower of two hundred horses,
O n goes the engine to start the race,
R ound the track faster and faster,
S peeding like a bullet from a gun,
C an't stop or you'll lose the race,
H ats flying in the wind,
E ngine off, it's the end of the race.

David Locke (9)
Oldfield Park Junior School

SANTA

Sleigh rider
Night glider
Booze drinker
Food nicker
Chimney sweeper
Pie eater
News reader
Animal lover.

Stephen Ralph (10)
Oldfield Park Junior School

WHAT IS BLUE?

Blue is the colour of the water sparkling bright,
Red is the colour of the velvety roses lying in the flower bed,
Yellow is the colour of the sun shining beautifully in the sky,
Purple is the colour of a plum that is very juicy inside,
Green is the colour of the grass growing low in the ground,
Black is the colour of a cat creeping along in the night,
White is the colour of paper until I write.

Natasha Harris (8)
Oldfield Park Junior School

A MORNING VIEW

I stood upon the hillside
Everything was still,
The birds were singing,
Owls were hooting,
The sun rose over the horizon,
You could smell the fresh air in the mid morning,
The frosty grass was slippery underfoot,
You could see everything clearly upon the hillside.

Sophie Drake (10)
Oldfield Park Junior School

IN MY BEDROOM

I go to bed, I see a shadow,
Big and spooky, it comes into my room,
So I put my head under my duvet,
I hear creeping and moaning and doors moving,
I take the duvet off my head,
Relief, it's only my brother.

Alex Hussey (9)
Oldfield Park Junior School

What Is Yellow?

Yellow is the colour of the sun high in the sky,
Yellow is the colour of a sunflower tall and bright,
Yellow is the colour of my pen colouring away,
Yellow is the colour of manerva winning the cup,
Yellow is the colour of paint splishing and splashing,
Yellow is the colour of my bike, big and speedy,
Yellow is the colour of a banana, swishy and big.

Tom Fry (9)
Oldfield Park Junior School

Fire

Fire is burning brightly in the house,
people are sitting by it trying to get warm.
Cats are sleeping by the fire
and so are dogs.
They are snuggled up warm,
the dogs are growling,
they are waking up the cats.

Katie Durbin (9)
Oldfield Park Junior School

The Great Storm

Lightning flashes!
Thunder crashes!
Rain splashing!
Rain bashing!
Wind whizzing!
The wind is calming down,
Now it's time to play.

Seb Burvill (9)
Oldfield Park Junior School

THE ALIEN INVASION

Flying saucers flying in all directions,
Aliens making people their slaves,
Alien spaceships destroying all the buildings in sight,
Bang! Bang! Bang!
The army are coming with tanks, planes, helicopters and cannons,
Army men throwing grenades at alien troops,
People are shouting out,
'Help! Help! Help!'
The army are too strong so the aliens teleport back into space.
It is over, half the city is destroyed but all the people are alive.
Hooray! Hooray! Hooray!

Craig Wall (9)
Oldfield Park Junior School

UNTITLED

Red is the colour of an apple,
eating it on the way to chapel.

Yellow is the colour of the sun,
it is too hot to run.

Green is the colour of the grass
blowing away in the wind.

Blue is the colour of the sky
with birds flying by.

Linda Liang Hu (9)
Oldfield Park Junior School

FLOWERS

I like flowers
There are lots of flowers in the world
There are different types of flower,
With flowers you could decorate.

There are lots of colour
Like pink, red, white, blue, yellow and purple,
You need to give water to flowers,
Flowers need sunlight, water and air.

If you have flowers in the garden it is beautiful,
Flowers do smell and have a scent,
Flowers are useful,
Flowers are so beautiful.

Cema Rahim (10)
Oldfield Park Junior School

SWIMMING

S   is for my friends *s*plashing water at me,
W   is for waves that wash me away,
I   is for increase of waves when people get in
M   is for me who splashes my mum
M   is for mats I stand on when I get out,
I   is for inconvenience we had at the swimming baths
N   is for nobody who plays with me.
G   is for Granny who comes with me.

William Robinson (9)
Oldfield Park Junior School

WHAT IS MULTICOLOURED?

What is yellow?
The sun is yellow shining in the sky.
What is blue?
The sea is blue splashing everywhere.
What is green?
The grass is green with flowers in-between.
What is red?
A tomato is red growing by the flower bed.
What is multicoloured?
A rainbow's multicoloured, just a rainbow.

Jessica Ball (9)
Oldfield Park Junior School

THE WITCH'S POTION

Dad's underwear
Two frog's legs,
Three mouldy sandwiches,
Seven robots' legs,
Two donkey's ears
Three bowls of mouldy cereal,
Seven mouldy biscuits,
Two camels' humps,
Three bats' wings.

What do you get?
Witch's delight.

Luca Elice (11)
Oldfield Park Junior School

DOWNSTAIRS AT NIGHT

At night it's dark
And creepy things lark
I thought I saw something furry
So I'd better hurry.

Hairs, hairs, everywhere
I bet it's coming from upstairs
I creep upstairs, nothing there
I only saw my teddy bear.

I go back downstairs
I see my dog
Playing with a wild hog
So I go upstairs to bed.

Hannah Latchem (10)
Oldfield Park Junior School

SANTA

He came down the chimney
On Christmas Day,
Giving lots of presents
Along the way.
He comes once a year,
Yet he watches every day,
He gave me presents this year,
Hip, hip hooray.

Lisa Ghosn (9)
Oldfield Park Junior School

RABBIT'S FUNERAL

Bury him deep,
down very deep.

Bury him peacefully,
down very peacefully.

No more chewing on a carrot,
No more hopping like a kangaroo,
No more grooming of his fur,
No more, no more.

Amy North (9)
Oldfield Park Junior School

THE STORM

It rumbles over the sea,
Destroying everything in its path,
Terrorising ships and planes,
Demolishing buildings and trees,
Yes! It's destroyed the school,
Oh no! It's coming towards my house.
My house has been destroyed.
Phew! It was only a dream!

James Butt (10)
Oldfield Park Junior School

MY DOG

My dog just sits rolling his eyes,
He's boring! Boring! Boring!
All he does is eat and drink and snore,
Boring! He is three years old and sits in front of the fire.

Kayleigh Pearson (9)
Oldfield Park Junior School

SPEEDBOAT

S peedboat zooming around the water.
P eople drive out of control,
E ngine working as fast as it can,
E ngine slowing, slower and slower,
D amage! We'd better get out,
B oat bumping up and down,
O n the speedboat people are jumping up and down,
A nother speedboat crashing into us,
T ime to go home.

Daniel Hughes (9)
Oldfield Park Junior School

THE BIG SPIDER

There's a big spider in my bedroom,
I can't help the spider,
It goes up and down my legs,
It feels like a tickly touch on my legs,
It goes up my walls,
It is like a web cage tied in my bed,
I'm not afraid of the spider.

Daniel Hopkins (9)
Oldfield Park Junior School

MY CAT TABBY

My cat, Tabby died last week, I was really sad,
We buried him and then sang hymns and prayed,
He died an ill cat,
He was really thin, he always hated to go to the vets,
The last time he went he was put down.

Sam Land (10)
Oldfield Park Junior School

TREASURE HUNT

I'm going on a treasure hunt to see what I can find,
I go into the spooky woods with a spade and a knife.
I find a spot and dig down deep, but nothing.
What shall I do?
I'll dig down,
down,
down
And look, what have I found? A treasure box!
I open it up and there I find some golden treasure
just for *me!*

Gemma Broad (9)
Oldfield Park Junior School

PLAYSTATION

P   eople cheering at the top of their voices
L   earning quickly, now playing,
A   nalogue control on the game pad
Y   acky driving down the street
S   teering round a sharp corner
T   he fun keeps coming
A   dding another player
T   antrum coming nearer
I   n the lead run
O   vertaking the leader
N   ow I have won the trophy!

Jason Poulton (10)
Oldfield Park Junior School

BULLIES

I cower away from them in a corner.
They don't let me play their games,
They whisper, giggle and call me names.
My feet are rooted to the ground.
I don't make a sound.
I am frozen to the spot as if I was made of stone.
I'm just standing there, all alone.
My throat is dry.
My eyes are watery, I want to cry.
My legs feel like jelly,
I have thousands of butterflies in my belly.
Finally, they let me go,
But they'll be back tomorrow I know.

Esme Haughton (10)
Oldfield Park Junior School

FIREWORKS

Fireworks are loud!
Fireworks are sparkly,
Fireworks are pretty,
Fireworks are light,
Fireworks are excellent,
Fireworks are super,
Fireworks are fantastic,
Fireworks are *the best!*

Kyle Norris (9)
Oldfield Park Junior School

WHEN YOU'RE TUCKED UP IN BED

When you're tucked up in bed,
The moon is glistening,
Foxes and hedgehogs looking for food,
All when you're tucked up in bed.

When you're tucked up in bed,
Owls are hooting, 'Tu-whit tu-woo'
And cars occasionally zooming by,
All when you're tucked up in bed.

When you're tucked up in bed all warm and asleep,
The stars are twinkling in the sky,
And you're dreaming in your sleep,
All when you're tucked up in bed.

When you're tucked up in bed,
The sun begins to rise,
So early in the morning,
All when you're tucked up in bed.

Amber Waldron-Ross (10)
Oldfield Park Junior School

MONSTER

M onster beside my bed all slimy and green,
O ctopus legs all green and horrible,
N ose all horrible covered with spots,
S illy stuck up hair, all greasy and wet,
T eeth all yellow,
E ars full of wax,
R ed spots on its face.

Chloe Norris (9)
Oldfield Park Junior School

TREASURE CHEST

There's a chest in the deep blue sea
It's twice as big as you and me,
It's twice as big as a fur coat
It's about the size of a speed boat,
In it there is silver and gold
It's all about one hundred years old.
The sharks have swept away the sand
And by the chest there's a skeleton hand,
We might find it, we might not
There might even be a pot,
You never know what you'll find
So do not get left behind.

James Mitchell (10)
Oldfield Park Junior School

BIRTHDAY

B   irthday, birthday, it's my birthday,
I   get up looking for my presents,
R   ight now my parents are getting up,
T   ime to go back to bed,
H   igh up on my bunk bed I'm getting more excited,
D   ownstairs are my presents,
A   t the side of my bed is a present,
Y   es, my friends are here to party.

Andrew Bean (9)
Oldfield Park Junior School

HELICOPTER

H   elicopter blades spinning round and round,
E   ngine working as fast as it can,
L   ight shining everywhere,
I   t's hovering in the air,
C   rashing towards the sea, 'Quick, put the life jackets on,'
O   ut of the helicopter we jump into the waves,
P   eople are swimming away,
T   hrashing through the ocean,
E   ngine blows up into flames,
R   acing away, 'Hurry!'

Ben Norris (9)
Oldfield Park Junior School

FAMILY

I've got a brother who's big,
And a sister who's small,
But it doesn't really matter if it's nothing at all.

I've got a dog that's young,
And a cat that's old,
And a house that is really, really cold.

I've got a mum who's pretty,
And a dad who's ugly,
But it doesn't really matter because they're my family.

Ashley Smith (10)
Oldfield Park Junior School

BULLIES

I am rooted to the ground,
They don't let me play their games,
I hear them giggle and laugh,
I feel like I'm going to explode like a firework,
My eyes feel like waterfalls,
Pushing against my eyelids,
My hands feel like rocks in my pockets,
I want to go home,
They come up to me,
They poke and push me,
I want the ground to swallow me up,
They finally leave.

Kelsie Davies (10)
Oldfield Park Junior School

WHAT AM I?

I am fluffy and soft,
I chase cats out of the garden,
I bark up trees,
I am brown and black,
I have long droopy ears,
I love to have my tummy rubbed,
I like to play with teddies,
I don't like squeaky toys,
What am I?

Lauren Blackmore (9)
Oldfield Park Junior School

THE BIG TEST

I woke up this morning in a really cold sweat,
I'm not going to pass you can bet,
I packed my bag and put on my last shoe,
Then I stormed out the door in a really bad mood.

I went in the playground and started to play,
This really good game with my best friend called Kay,
The whistle was blowing and people were flowing,
Into the cloakroom at last.

We sat down in our seats
And got handed a sheet
The test had begun
I felt like I wasn't going to pass.

I started to fight through it
Just one more question to write,
So I wrote it down fast,
And I got the best mark in the class.

Laura Ollis (10)
Oldfield Park Junior School

THE BIG THING

It's so big, no so huge, maybe
Even . . . ginormous.
But I'm not afraid,
Yes I am.
Run, run, run away it's the
Ant, the terrifying ant
From the garden. Run
For your life.

Josh Reynolds (9)
Oldfield Park Junior School

IN THE CAR

The car is running
We're going on holiday.
I am hot and bothered.
'Are we there yet?'
I keep shouting
'No!' they say.
'How long till we're there?'
'An hour and a half!'
'Ohhhh!'
Finally, we get there
We go to the caravan
I sit on the seat
My mum is getting the stuff out the car
She comes in to the caravan
And I am asleep, snoring
Ohhh . . .
I wanted to go to the restaurant.

Josh Nash (10)
Oldfield Park Junior School

COLOURS

Red makes me feel warm,
Blue makes me feel cold.
Green makes me feel excited,
Yellow makes me feel silly.
Orange makes me feel sick,
Black makes me feel bored.
Purple makes me feel dizzy,
I hate purple!

Steven Wilkins (11)
Oldfield Park Junior School

A YEAR

Spring

The spring is wet
It is raining all day
It's green.

Summer

It's very hot
There is no water here
Too hot.

Autumn

Leaves are falling
They are very brown leaves
It is getting colder out here
Go home.

Winter

Very cold here
The river has iced up
We can't go fishing, it is cold,
Too cold.

Gabriel Sky-Jones (11)
Oldfield Park Junior School

I WISH

I wish I was a bird so I could fly up high in the night sky.
I wish I was a baby so I could get picked up all the time.
I wish I was a bee buzzing around in the bright sky.
I wish I was old because I'd get more love and care.
I wish.

Georgina Dellow (8)
Oldfield Park Junior School

THE AEROPLANE

A great, black, 1000 mph eagle,
The giant carnivore of the skies.
You can hear the aero engines,
Ringing in your ears,
Like the roar of a lion or a chimpanzee.
The beast is as graceful as a cat,
As fast as a cheetah,
And as deadly as a viper.
One moment it is stealthy,
And then it attacks,
Like a tiger attacking its prey.
Too late, you see it come,
Like a hawk diving at a mouse.
It seems to have a mind of its own,
It seems to have an independent brain,
And man seems so small,
Compared to this giant,
The terror of the skies!

Ben Sixsmith (11)
Oldfield Park Junior School

WET PLAYTIME

It's wet outside so we can't go out,
We'll stay in without a doubt.
Two boys are fighting and two girls are doing their hair,
But what is this? Four girls not being fair.
I can't wait till the end of the day!
Hold on a moment,
The whistle is going to go.

Alex Webb (10)
Oldfield Park Junior School

THE MONSTER

There's a monster in my room,
He's really big and scary.
He doesn't like my mum and dad,
My brother doesn't believe me.
I tried to talk to him once,
Though he didn't reply.
I haven't seen him, only his shadow,
I don't know what colour he is.
He's coming out,
He's, he's . . . a mouse!
Eek, eek!

I don't believe it,
It's just a small white blob.
It's going out of the room,
It's really fast.
I've got to get it before Mum sees it.
Ahhhhh!
Too late!

Eloise Collins (10)
Oldfield Park Junior School

MY DOG

My dog is black and white
And howls in the night.
If he doesn't have his tea
Then he will start to pester me.

My dog is fast at last
Because he used to be slow
Good job he is fast
Or he will be the last.

My dog is clumsy
And his name is Monty
He climbs on my table
And falls asleep.

Daniel Mardon (10)
Oldfield Park Junior School

THE MUTANT CHEESE BURGER

I roam the streets.
For monsters like me,
Two eyes and two relishes,
A belly button a pea.
Onions for teeth,
Lettuce for lips,
I'm a mutant cheese burger,
My ears are two chips.

I need a friend,
Oh what should I do?
Perhaps a mutant toilet brush
Blocking up the loo.
I search for a friend,
But where could one be?
I know, a mutant pebble
Washed up from the sea!
At last! I have found one!
A friend just for me!
He's a mutant sand rock
Who named himself Lee!

Jay Gormley (10)
Oldfield Park Junior School

THE NIGHT DETECTIVE

One night,
Where a crime has been.
I went to investigate the scene.

Being the night detective isn't easy,
Knowing all the crooks are after you,
Especially when you're nine years old.
Whatever shall I do?

The criminal has left no trace,
Of any kind of clue.
Apart from a single hair,
Which was completely blue.

Soon I realised the obvious answer,
Of who left the clue.
It was none other than
My older cousin Sue.

But what was she doing here?
She doesn't live in this street.
But then this is the time of year
When we all meet.

Suddenly, I woke up,
It was all a dream.
But it looked so true,
From what it seems.

Yiran Tang (10)
Oldfield Park Junior School

LIFE ON A PIRATE SHIP

Running up the shaking decks,
Hearing the cannons fire upon the enemy,
Hearing pirates scream and shout,
Banging, creaking, musket shots.
Fire the cannons! Fire the cannons!
Caboom! Smash! Bang!
Wood flying everywhere
'No mercy,' shouts the captain,
Destroy them! Let no one live!
'Board their ship, take their treasure,
Sink their ship,
Victory, victory!'

Calum Macey (10)
Oldfield Park Junior School

DOLPHINS

Dolphins jumping in and out of the sea
You wouldn't believe it if you were me,
They have a lot of fun
When they bathe in the sun,
Dolphins splashing all around
Making their flippers touch the sea ground
Racing to get some food
When they have some they feel good,
Fishes swimming underneath
Dolphins swimming to the bottom of the sea.

Louise Cox (10)
Oldfield Park Junior School

ON THE BOAT

The boat is rocking backwards and forwards,
Water is flooding the deck.
People are soaked and want to get off and go home.
The thunderstorm starts,
The rain falls down hard.
Everyone is cold and shivering,
And want to get inside.
If it keeps on going we will be overflowing.
The water is being bailed out of the boat,
The children are crying,
I have a sore throat.

Luke Boughey (11)
Oldfield Park Junior School

NERVOUS

Oh no, it's the year six show,
I was shaking like a leaf
My heart was pounding
My heart was thumping
I went bright red
My hands felt like rocks in my pocket
I was singing all on my own
I didn't think it was good
But everyone clapped,
Phew, it's over.

Claire Higgins (11)
Oldfield Park Junior School

Up, Down, All Around

The match is on, the title is up,
It's time to try and win the cup.
So up goes the bat and up goes the ball,
If we lose we are gonna eat gruel.
But yes, down go the bails, up goes the finger,
Cheers echo all around,
Bowler static batsman wondering
Why didn't I stick with stopping traffic.
But it's too late now. *Pow!* Next batsman in his crease.
An hour later next team in next ball bowled. *Crack!*
'Where is the ball?'
'Here it is, says the man with a dent in his head.
Umpire signals six. Moments later balls are flying,
Fielders crying. Bat swings back like anti-aircraft
Then forward. *Smack!* The ball begins to show a crack
And yes, 'Six!' We've won.

Luke Hilferty (10)
Oldfield Park Junior School

A Monster's Menu

Men's legs
Turtle heads
Chicken eyes
Rotten pies
Birds' droppings
Tomatoes slopping
Donkeys' guts
Pigs' huts
That's a monster's menu!

Joseph Aldous (10)
Oldfield Park Junior School

THERE'S SOMETHING UNDER MY BED

There's something under my bed
But I don't know what,
I think it's a monster
I hope it is not

I look under my bed
It has furry feet
I hope it doesn't pop out on me
I wouldn't like to meet

It has furry arms
It has a fat tummy
I wish I wasn't up here
I wish I was with my mummy

I go over to my bed
He says I want a nice juicy boy
I lift up my bed covers and
Aaaagh . . . it's only my toy.

Lauren Tolley (10)
Oldfield Park Junior School

THE MATCH

I walk to the dressing room
Shaking with fear as I hear the crowd cheer.

As I put on my kit there is a knock on the door
It is my team saying, 'Come on.'

I walk on the pitch sweating like a bull
Waving to the crowd sitting on the wall.

I can't believe it, we won the match!
With a kick of the ball they lost the match.

As I leave the pitch I clenched the cup
And say to my team, 'We won the cup.'

Luke Gimson (10)
Oldfield Park Junior School

THE MONSTER

I woke up in middle of the night
All tucked up in my bed,
I suddenly heard a creak outside my room,
It scared me to death!

In the morning I told my mum everything I heard,
She said, 'Oh it's just a mouse,
There's nothing to be scared of!'
I also told my sister Emma,
'Well, what do you think it is?' she said.
'I think it's a monster,' I exclaimed.
Emma just laughed.

The hours passed by
And I had to go to bed
When it was eleven o'clock.

I went out to investigate,
I suddenly heard another creak,
So I ran downstairs,
Something was there,
I turned on the light,
Arrgghh . . . it's some mice.

Kay Durham (10)
Oldfield Park Junior School

AT THE WEDDING

I have got butterflies in my tummy,
I am shaking like an unset jelly,
I am so nervous it will all go wrong.

Everyone arrives at the church.
We are all sitting down then in comes the bride and groom.
My heart is pounding at the fastest possible rate,
I am sitting extremely worried at the back,
Then suddenly I hear the vicar say,
'Does anybody oppose this happy marriage?'
I sat up the best I could hoping all would go well.
Then he said,
'I now pronounce you husband and wife.'
In the evening we went to a do
It was a very happy marriage.

Zack Muir (10)
Oldfield Park Junior School

TREASURE HUNT

I wonder where the treasure could be
Looking across the deep blue sea,
But what if it is not there
If I find it we will have to handle with care.
So I start to dig down and down,
Then I felt a bony hand . . . Argh!
It was just a skeleton hand
Then I saw the chest sat there,
Yes, I have found it!
I opened up the chest and there was nothing there.

Jonathan Baker (10)
Oldfield Park Junior School

NERVOUS

My legs are shaking like unset jelly.
I've got butterflies in my belly.
I can't believe I'm going out there.
Sometimes life is not very fair.
Think of all those people watching me.
Before I go on I must have a cup of tea.
Now the moment is here.
It's time to get rid of my fear.
Hooray, it went all right.
The competition was tight.

Joe Kenward (10)
Oldfield Park Junior School

HIDDEN TREASURE

I was sat in bed then I dropped off.
I dreamt I was on a desert island.
I was with my friends, we got chased by monkeys,
Then I found a cave, it was really dark and scary.
Me and my friends found a big pile of dirt and a brush
So we brushed the dirt off
And found a treasure chest,
We opened it and there was
Chocolate, sweets, gold, rubies,
Comics, pearls, everything nice,
Then I heard a voice saying,
'Wake up, wake up.'
Then I opened my eyes
And there stood my mum
It was only then I realised it was a dream.

Hannah Phillips (8)
St John's RC Primary School

HIDDEN TREASURE

Once I found a map,
It was a treasure map.
So I started the next day
It was a long way.
I was in a wood
And I put up my hood,
It had started to rain
And that was a pain.
I was building a house
And I came across a mouse.
It said, 'Can I live with you?
I promise I won't poo.'
'I'm going on a quest,' I said,
'Are you a pest?'
'No, I'm a mouse
And I need a house.'
'Come with me
I'm going to the sea.'
Next day we climbed a mountain
And we drank from a fountain.
I saw a cave by the name of St Dave,
We went inside, it was dark
And I wanted to hide.
Then we found the treasure
I did a measure
150cm by 4ft.
It was full of gold
More than I could hold,
Then I went home.

Natalya James (8)
St John's RC Primary School

THE PIRATES

One day I was at the seaside,
In the sea, in my boat.
Then suddenly, a wave came,
And knocked off my coat.
I changed into my swimming trunks
And jumped off the boat.
I grabbed them just in time,
And got back on the boat.
Then suddenly I realised
That I had gone far out to sea,
I was so surprised,
That I banged my knee.
I watched the beach go faraway,
I said, 'Goodbye sunny bay.'
Then I suddenly saw a ship,
It looked to me like a pirate ship.
I sailed over to it,
Then I saw the pirates,
They shouted at me,
And I shouted back,
Then I saw something white,
Then I realised it was a cat.
I climbed aboard and found a gun,
I shot every man that was on board.
I went down through the hatch
And found loads of treasure,
Now I am so rich,
The money gives me tons of pleasure.

Joel Pope (9)
St John's RC Primary School

HIDDEN TREASURE

I'm going on an adventure,
I'm going to pack my bag,
I'm going to pack it good.
I'm gonna pack it with lots of food.
I'm going on a trip today, a hot journey,
February or March or May.
Oh look at that high mountain.
When I got up the top
I wanted a drink from the fountain.
When it got dark with no light
I slept in a cave through the night.
I went through loads of lakes,
It's good I didn't see any snakes.
Oh no, there's a snake in the stream,
Oh thank goodness, it was just a dream.

Hannah White (8)
St John's RC Primary School

HIDDEN TREASURE

In the night
We turned on the light,
We opened the door,
We jumped over the gate,
We went to a pyramid,
And we got the treasure
And the mummy.

George Cox (8)
St John's RC Primary School

MUMMY QUEST

High in the Egyptian deserts
In the pyramids of Sylini
Did the slaves work for him
Dig a tunnel to the ancient chamber
Now get the scrolls.

Then some people nicked them
Ram the walls, the chambers in there
End of the line, guards over there
And they were trapped.
Slash, slash, they got hurt by swords
Under the chamber laid the treasure
'Run' called the slaves, it's a trap,
It's collapsing
And the chamber was never found again.

Tom Morris (8)
St John's RC Primary School

HIDDEN TREASURE

I know it's hidden somewhere,
Somewhere far away, I'm going to start today,
I'm going to the place where I knew my way would be barred.
I told you so, I told you I knew it would be hard.
I'm climbing up a tree, I can see the cave
But I can see that the knave is before the cave.
I've found it, I've got it, a garden gnome,
Oh dear, now I have to go home!

Emma Scolding (7)
St John's RC Primary School

HIDDEN TREASURE

Seven years ago I went to Egypt
I found some treasure, it was . . .
Lace, all sorts of material,
Lace of course,
Velvet, cottonwool, nylon.
Emma, my friend said today
'I like your socks'
Really it was the lace that I found.

Maybe next summer
I'll go there again.

Emer Heatley (7)
St John's RC Primary School

TREASURE

I love treasure
Rubies, diamonds
I love treasure
Gold, silver
I love treasure
Crowns, rings
I love treasure
Sparkling treasure
I love treasure
Every treasure
I love treasure.

Sidonie Travers (8)
St John's RC Primary School

I'M OFF TO FIND TREASURE

One day I was at the seaside
Sitting in my boat,
Then a shark came along
And knocked off my lucky float.

Five minutes later
I'd thought I'd take a swim,
So I put on my swimming stuff
And jumped right in.

Then I went underwater and it was so calm,
Then I saw something brown and big,
But not like a farm.

Then I went closer it looked like a chest,
And when I opened it
There was a crown and dress.

So then I took the crown and dress
And swam back up to the surface of the sea,
Then I climbed onto the boat and said,
'Phew, that's enough for me.'

Eilis Barrett (8)
St John's RC Primary School

BOOKS

Good books make us glad,
They show many mysteries,
Some can show the past.

Ryan Tainton (8)
St John's RC Primary School

THE HIDDEN TREASURE

Hidden under the deep blue sea,
Glistens treasures beyond this world,
No one has ever seen these treasures
And is a secret of the underworld.

These treasures I speak of are in the deepest depths,
They are existing ancient treasures
And are most beautiful
And belong to the underworld.

If you try to steal these treasures you will not succeed,
Instead you will be confronted
By three most dangerous great whites
Circling dawn till dusk.

Now be gone my friend
And never mention these treasures to anyone
As it is a sworn secret of the underworld.

Jack Watson (9)
St John's RC Primary School

BURIED TREASURE

I wonder where the treasure is
Let's look behind a tree
I wonder where the treasure is
Let's look behind the bush
I wonder where the treasure is
Let's look behind the rock
Oh look, a cross
Looks like we've found treasure,
Let's dig!

Thomas Southcott (8)
St John's RC Primary School

HIDDEN TREASURE

Hidden treasure under the sea,
I see, I see!
The sea bubbles and cuddles,
I see, I see!

The waves crash on the sea,
I see, I see!
The treasure comes up from the sea,
I see, I see!

But the hidden treasure
Lies quiet, under the sea.

Aidan Kalsi (9)
St John's RC Primary School

HIDDEN TREASURES

I went on a ship to see, see, see
What was on the bottom of the deep blue sea.
I looked all around me and all I could see
Were plunders of rocks all over me.

I went to a ship to see, see, see
What was on the deep blue sea,
But I found a brown, brown box sealed with gold
And I thought it was treasure.

I opened the brown, brown box
And there it was,
The beautiful treasure at my side.

Larry Warman (9)
St John's RC Primary School

MAGIC BOX

Search around this magic box,
Surrounded with special locks.
Can there be a ballerina dancing,
Or a light-winged fairy prancing?
It might be full of buried treasure,
That will bring me so much pleasure.
What can be in this magic box,
All surrounded with special locks?
The magic box is very old,
Within my hand I gently hold.
Inside the box there might be a magical wood,
Or a ray of hope and good.
Can there be a black moon,
Or a chime for midnight, which will be soon?
I gently open the box in my hands,
And I have a little tiny peep,
But then I hear a creak
So I close the box and pretend to sleep.
Then I try to get up with a great big leap,
And reveal the glow of magic that lights my face.
But the magic box is still safe,
In the box I think I see a touch of frost,
Or a maze to get lost.
But in the box there is treasure,
And now at last, I'm filled with pleasure.

Cassandra Moll (10)
St John's RC Primary School

PIRATE SHIP

I went through time for some treasure,
As I flowed through time I felt like a feather.

I ended up on a pirate ship
I wondered if they had pizza and chips?

A pirate said they were looking for treasure
It was no size that you could measure.

My eyes lit up like golden rings
Thinking about all the lovely things.

We went to dig in the sand
We had a lovely brass band.

I found the treasure in a box
It couldn't fit inside my socks.

I rode back home
All alone.

With the treasure in my hand
To my home land.

I opened the box with a skeleton key
And wondered what I will see?

To my amazement and surprise
Dog biscuits were before my eyes.

Hannah Walsh (9)
St John's RC Primary School

DRAGON AND THE TREASURE

There was a dragon in a castle,
With fire around it,
He had a treasure box,
With gold around it,
And silver coins in it,
One in a packet and one in a purse.

He watched the treasure day and night,
With eyes as big as a marble.

There were robbers coming at night-time,
Trying to get the treasure.
But the dragon with his two eyes,
As big as a marble,
He watched and watched day and night,
So nobody could dare to go and get the treasure.

And if he didn't die
The treasure would still be watched.

Angela Kohn (9)
St John's RC Primary School

THE RING

'Tis a sunny day of spring
but I have lost my precious ring.
I am inside all the day
but I have still to look that way.

I will look under the table
if only I am able.
And all I find is a spoon,
in the round shape of the moon.

I have looked everywhere by now
and all I've found is a spoon and a cuddly cow.
Alas, my ring has disappeared
but I have treasured it all these years.

Chrissy Forestell (9)
St John's RC Primary School

CHOCOLATE TREASURE

I'm the little girl
who loves chocolate,
and I lock it up
in my pocket.

I'm the little girl
who had the weirdest birthday,
and I'll never forget
that day.

My mum hid a treasure
and I didn't know what it was
but I knew
it was something I love.

I found the treasure
when I thought it would be never,
I was really, really stuck
and down on my luck.

When my mum handed it over,
I thought to myself
Chocolate . . . chocolate . . .
Chocolate!

Joana Figueira (10)
St John's RC Primary School

HIDDEN TREASURE FOUND

H idden under the ground,
I n a secret cave,
D eep beneath the mountains.
D ip down,
E ach time you enter.
N ever make a sound.

T rickling water
R uns around the cave.
E verlasting water,
A mbushed by rocks,
S o be careful.
U nder the biggest rock,
R each for the gems,
E ach one for everlasting life.

F ind your way back,
O ver the rocks.
U p above there is a key,
N ear the entrance,
D eep beneath the mountains.

Peter Bale (9)
St John's RC Primary School

HIDDEN TREASURES

I made a beautiful model
Of bricks, red, white and blue
It stood so tall and regal
I'd fixed it together with glue.

I wish you could've seen it,
It really captured your eye,
But I had to hide it away from my brother
In a cupboard way up high.

I made a paper aeroplane
So light and swift and white
It soared up to the ceiling
At the speed of light.

My friend flew that precious aeroplane
And liked it very much.
Then I hid my special treasure
From all hands that could touch.

Jack Griffiths (10)
St John's RC Primary School

GO AND OPEN THE DOOR

Go and open the door
maybe you'll see rolling hills
or children playing
or the golden sun shining.

Go and open the door
maybe outside there's a waterfall
or babies laughing and giggling
or a kitten with a ball of string.

Go and open the door
maybe there's a land of sweets
or a land full of autumn colours
green, red, orange, yellow and brown.

Go and open the door
maybe there's a wood full of animals
or sparkling stars in the night
or bright, red sunset in the evening.

Go and open the door . . .

Laura Stevenson (11)
St John's RC Primary School

HIDDEN TREASURES

In ancient Egypt
While I was on holiday,
I found a treasure.

I was on a dig
With some archaeologists
I tripped on a stone.

It was black as night
Hidden from eyes in the sand.
We began to search.

We dug down and down
To find an immense statue.
It was Anubis!

He was the dog god,
Keeper of the underworld.
This was his temple.

After many years
The site was excavated
And now stands proudly

For the world to see
People may marvel at him
In his dark glory.

That is why today
I and others travel there
Constantly seeking.

The hidden treasures
That lie beneath the great sands
Of age-old Egypt.

Adam Arscott (9)
St John's RC Primary School

THE HIDDEN TREASURE

One summer's day
Three boys went away.

They camped by the sea
And had toast for tea.

When morning came
They played a game.

They ran on the beach
And kicked the ball out of reach.

They looked high and low
Then saw down below.

A big dark cave
Near a crashing wave.

They crept nervously in
And grazed their skin.

Then one of them saw
A big large door.

They opened it wide
And there inside

Was a large chest
And on it was a crest

They went to the police station
And gave them information.

Now that the hidden treasure was found
The police gave them one whole pound.

Nathaniel Scott (9)
St John's RC Primary School

HIDDEN TREASURE

Down the road is a river,
Across the river is an island,
In the island is a wood,
Inside the wood is a house,
In the house there is a dark, dark room,
And in that dark room is a box,
In that box there is a
Bat! Ahhhh!

Shut the box,
Out the room,
Close the door,
Back through the woods,
In the boat,
Up the road and
In the house.
Let's not go there again in a hurry.

Isabelle Cundy (9)
St John's RC Primary School

HIDDEN TREASURES

Hidden treasures are jewels,
Like diamonds in the sky.
Stars dropped into the ocean
By God's hand.
Pirates' treasure lost in a shipwreck,
Fallen to the bottom of the sea.
Covered for thousands of years
In dark, wet sands.
Lost, all lost
In the deep, blue sea.

Charles Hall (11)
St John's RC Primary School

TREASURE ISLAND

Now I'm taking a good look at this map,
That I stole when Black Dog's gang were having a nap.
It goes through thick forests and rivers,
All of that gives me the quivers.
Well, I suppose I'd better give it a try,
Though I'll probably die.
Who can be my crew?
They will have to be true,
Maybe Joe and Nick, or John and Drew.
So many decisions to make,
It is no piece of cake.
And it's definitely not just a coup,
Perhaps I will just leave it to you.

Michael Prest (10)
St John's RC Primary School

LOST RING

I wonder where my mum's ring went?
It may be in the garden tent.
It may be still on holiday,
In the south of Spain,
Or, maybe it's gone to Scotland,
On the all-night train.
Maybe it's in the garden,
Hidden by a tree.
There's my mum's wedding ring,
Shining back at me.
Some people say it's hidden treasure,
But my mum calls it real pleasure!

Natalia Rozario (9)
St John's RC Primary School

HIDDEN TREASURES

I lifted my sandbag eyes,
And as I opened them I saw
The moon with its crescent-top head
And its bumpy-hill surface,
The spirits of the stars
Bursting open with wonder,
The stone-cold planets
With icy winds and lurching pain.
Our Milky Way wishing, washing,
Swaying to and fro.
I saw pitch-blackness up there.
Another world;
A place where you will live for eternity.
A mighty roar came out of the heavens.
Boom! Another portal to another dimension.
The sweet-centered Earth so kind.
Up we go, up higher and higher until . . .
We too closed our eyes,
And became the hidden treasures.

Thomas Rowland (10)
St John's RC Primary School

UNDER MY BED

Under my bed is a scary place,
I'm sure you would agree,
But I'm sure there's a treasure there,
Let's have a look and see.

A lot of stuff is under there,
Let's see what I might find,
Dirty socks and undershirts,
And junk of every kind.

But underneath all of the junk,
A treasure might be found,
If I dig deep enough,
I might find a pound.

Not only a pound I found,
But there was plenty more,
I kept digging deeper still
And there were fifty-four.

Shannon Farrell (10)
St John's RC Primary School

HIDDEN TREASURE

Captain Black Patch, a pirate,
Was shipwrecked on an island.
He buried his treasure
Where no one could find it,
And made a map to remember
Before being rescued.

A long time passed,
Two hundred years in fact.
His great-great-great-great grandson
Found a secret drawer in his desk.

In the drawer was the map.
He set sail straightaway
To find the island.
After days of searching,
He found the island
And the map led him to
The hidden treasure.

Emily Francis (9)
St John's RC Primary School

DEEP SEA DIVING

Deep sea diving in the sea,
Finding hidden treasure,
Looking at the fishes swim
In the deep sea water.

Finding hidden shipwrecks and treasure
In the deep waters.
Pearls, rubies, diamonds and emeralds,
Lots of treasure everywhere.

Sharks are circling
In the water,
Rippling the surface with their fins,
Hidden treasure everywhere.

Frankie Stratton (10)
St John's RC Primary School

THE MYSTERY BOOK

Books are dusty and
Some are not. Lots are legends
And most are stories.

Rhianne Bolton (9)
St John's RC Primary School

WONDERFUL SEEDS

Growing into plants
For everybody to see
Cheer up our gardens.

Daniel Keevill (9)
St John's RC Primary School

THE HIDDEN TREASURES OF THE BIN

Do you know what lies within
That stinky, smelly kitchen bin?
Have you ever looked down there?
I bet 'til now, you didn't care.
If you put your face right in,
You'd see the hidden treasure of the bin.
Surprisingly, it doesn't reek,
But trust me, it's been there more than a week.
And other people wouldn't know,
Cos that's as far as scientists go.
They wouldn't want people through thick and thin,
Thinking there's something nice in a bin!

Sylvia Bevan (9)
St John's RC Primary School

SPIDERS

They creep here and there,
Making cobwebs in your house,
Catching pesky flies.

John Partridge (8)
St John's RC Primary School

TREES

Trees are nice to have,
Lovely colours, orange, red,
Trees have love like me.

Manon Le Garnec (9)
St John's RC Primary School

THE HIDDEN TREASURES OF MY GARDEN

Winter has passed
Spring has come
I walk into my garden to find
A sea of sapphire bluebells
And an arch of ruby-red roses
All surrounded with
Necklaces of daisies
And tulip goblets.

The sun shines on the
Golden trumpets of daffodils
Great plates of sunflowers
And the dubloons of dandelions
All laid out on a
Carpet of emeralds.
These are the hidden treasures
Of my garden.

Jessica Warlow (11)
St John's RC Primary School

HIDDEN TREASURES

We set off in the morning
In search of a treasure,
How far we would travel
I couldn't measure.

The day was not fine
As we set off on our way,
Little did we know
It would be fun anyway.

We found the location
Where the treasure was buried,
We couldn't move one step further
Even if we hurried.

The box was so big,
The treasure was great,
If we stayed there to count it
We'd surely be late.

Ryan Farrell (10)
St John's RC Primary School

HIDDEN TREASURES

Beep . . . beep . . . beep
I wake up to the sound
Of the clock, the alarm clock.
I get out of bed
And open my curtains.
It is a sunny morning.
I get washed and dressed
And then sit at my dressing table
And brush my hair.
I open the top drawer
And take out my silver box,
A special present
Given to me on my birthday.
This contains my sparkly butterfly hairclips -
My hidden treasure.

Victoria Dent (9)
St John's RC Primary School

THE LITTLE, BIG PRESENT

I wonder what is in this tiny box?
Is it a cricket
Or maybe a goldfish?
What about a mouse with no tail?

I wonder what is in this tiny box?
I think a rabbit without any whiskers
Or maybe a squirrel with a bushy tail.

But once and for all
Let's find out
What is in this tiny box.
It is a . . . big . . . grey . . . elephant!

Rosie Dunn (10)
St John's RC Primary School

SEEDS

Seeds sprouting from soil,
Sprouting into a flower,
Bees collect nectar.

Maria Wong (8)
St John's RC Primary School

MYSTERY OF THE BOOK

Here is a great book
And it's from the library.
Wonder what's in it?

Jack Chalmers (8)
St John's RC Primary School

DUSK

By the big, old oak tree I sat,
Watching squirrels play in the grass,
Twisting, twirling, chasing tails,
Searching for their nuts in the dust.

Birds are flitting over tall trees,
Swooping gracefully over grass,
Sun casting shadows through the trees,
Bright rays of light thrown on the ground.

A breath of wind blew in the trees,
A spiral of leaves in the air.
Earth has many hidden treasures.

Rachel Prest (11)
St John's RC Primary School

BOOKS, BOOKS, BOOKS

Standing on the shelf
Lies information you need.
Pick a book, go on.

Anna Piercy (9)
St John's RC Primary School

BOOKS, BOOKS, BOOKS

Locked in libraries,
Lots of information and
Excitement - pick one.

Joseph Roberts (8)
St John's RC Primary School

THE WAITING TREASURE

I'm waiting for something,
I'm waiting to be found by a lucky man.
My walls contain gold, diamonds and pearls.
One day, one year, I'll be found.
My riches will be spent on happiness.
I'll continue waiting here,
I don't know how long for,
But I will be found
And then my riches will begin to end.

Patrick Crook (11)
St John's RC Primary School

HIDDEN TREASURES

Everyone wants them
But they are probably way too far.
They might be on an island
Or hidden in a sea.
No one knows where
The hidden treasures could be.

Victoria Cummings (10)
St John's RC Primary School

SEEDS

Seeds in the soil,
Everything dark and cold,
The flower is done.

Joseph Marchant (9)
St John's RC Primary School

HIDDEN TREASURE

I swim through the bottomless waters
Of the terrifying, rough sea.
I pass lonely grottos
Where nothing lives.

I swim ever closer
To my life.
Shadows of the murky waters
Tremble at my knees.

Light absorbs me,
Is my friend.
I fill the sea with hope.
I am light.
Light is a friend to me.

Anthony McLaughlin (11)
St John's RC Primary School

FANTASTIC BOOKS

Book are very nice,
Parents read to their children,
They're lots of fun.

George Cox (8)
St John's RC Primary School

THE HIDDEN WORLD

Under the dark earth,
Little creatures sleep unseen,
Shaded from the sun.

Eleanor Parker (8)
St John's RC Primary School

HIDDEN TREASURE

In the night I could hear
Fairies whispering in my ear.
'Come this way,' I heard them say
And from my bed they pulled me away.
'Where are you taking me?' I cried,
'We're going to Fern Valley,' the leader replied.
In one moment I was up in the air,
Up in the sky, as if I hadn't a care.
The lights looked like glitter sprinkled over the town,
We glided and soared and then we swooped down.
I floated down on fairies' wings to where a moonbeam lit up a cave,
'Go inside,' the fairies said, 'there's something inside you must
keep and save.'
I ventured inside, feeling excited and scared,
There inside a golden rose lay on a stone and glared.
My heart missed a beat as with joy I cried,
'Thank you, thank you, my fairy friends,' and then one sighed.
Worriedly I asked, 'Why did you sigh? What's wrong?'
'It's time to go back, we've been here nearly all night long.'
With sad faces they picked me up and flew me back home to bed,
Gripping my golden rose, 'Thank you,' I said.

Bethanie Locke (10)
St John's RC Primary School

CHANGING

Butterflies change from
Caterpillars, they make me
Think of summer days.

Samuel Sherry (8)
St John's RC Primary School

HUNT FOR THE TREASURE

There was a story my dad told me,
About some hidden treasure,
That would bring me great excitement
And also lots of pleasure.

I wonder if the map I've found
Will lead me to this place,
Where many risks I'll overcome
And dangers I will face.

I'll start upon my quest today,
My compass at the ready,
I've packed my bag with all I'll need,
My nerves I'll need to steady.

The journey will be long and tough,
But I am brave and strong.
I do hope I will find it soon,
Because Mum said, 'Don't be long.'

To see all of my island,
I will climb the apple tree,
Then maybe I will see from there,
The place I need to be.

Oh yes! I see, 'X' marks the spot,
It's not too far from here.
I'll climb the mountain, cross the swamp,
I know the treasure's near.

I've moved away the big stone pot,
And there to my surprise,
The treasure I had hoped to find,
Was there before my eyes.

Joel Bassett (10)
St John's RC Primary School

THE QUEST

The golden sun glistens in scarlet waters,
The sand gets in between my toes.
I dive, the water washes through my ears,
The fish zoom past me.
My air bubbles pop as they reach the surface,
An octopus lying in a shipwreck.
Out of the corner of my eye,
I see it - a twinkling box.
I open it and cover my eyes as the gold shines,
It's the end of my quest.

James Creese (10)
St John's RC Primary School

SEEDS

Seeds grow into trees,
They are grown by kind people,
Trees grow juicy pears.

Maisie McEvoy (8)
St John's RC Primary School

BOOKS

Happy fairy tales,
While children listen to Mum,
Till they fall asleep.

Jack Davies (9)
St John's RC Primary School

THE DISAPPOINTMENT

One day I found a book
And in this book I found a note
And this note said
'I know where some treasure is:
Get a slice of bread
Cut it into four pieces
Throw each piece as far as you can
Then jump on the piece that went the furthest'.
So I did what it said and I found a treasure chest
I opened it up but all there was inside was a grape.
I had been tricked!

Rowland Goodbody (8)
St John's RC Primary School

THE GROWING SEEDS

Seeds grow to flowers,
They are such beautiful things,
With nectar for bees.

Joshua Carey (8)
St John's RC Primary School

UNDERWATER

Hidden under seas
Lie beautiful coral reefs
I would like to see.

Andrew Eades (8)
St John's RC Primary School

HDDEN TREASURES

There are hidden treasures all over the house
And some are taken by a mouse.
Sometimes back to his hole
Goes something as big as a bowl.
He finds some things in the weirdest places,
Including a set of some braces.
One day he brought back the weirdest thing,
He brought back home a pig's nose ring.
Off a wall he took a plaque,
He even took the Union Jack.
When he was young he met a mouse
And he stole her small doll's house.
He works so hard without a rest,
But humans think he's just a pest.

Bruce Coram (9)
St John's RC Primary School

A KENNING

Gold,
Sparkly, amazing,
Silver, beautiful, lovely,
Nice, in a box, in a chest,
Toys, gold, silver, clothes, money,
Dangers, hard work,
Getting clues.

Did you get it?
Yes, hidden treasures.

Alice Piekarski (8)
St John's RC Primary School

HIDDEN TREASURES

The wind's at its very peak,
Even our boats spring a leak.
The waves crash up and down,
We are very wary because we may drown.
We're on our search to find our goal,
We may bail out before we lose all the coal.
We have sailed for miles on end,
But it seems like we're just going around the bend.
We've learnt the map like the back of our hand,
But if we reach our life's treasure, it's only as God planned.

Sam Kelson (11)
St John's RC Primary School

MAGICAL TREASURE

I walk on the beach
After some time I stumble
On the best treasure.

Douglas Kelly (10)
St John's RC Primary School

PIRATES

There is a pirate over there
sailing the seas for treasure,
joining more pirates
but looking forever.

Oliver Hawthorne (7)
St John's RC Primary School

A Knight In Shining Armour

There once was a knight
He was sent to a castle to fight a dragon.
The dragon was guarding the treasure.

When the knight had killed the dragon
He took the treasure, he was so thirsty
He went to a pond and drank some clean water.

He found a swan and thought for a minute or two.
He picked up the swan and took it to the king.

He said to the king, 'I bring this swan for you
And the other knights that are hungry.'

Brenden King (8)
St John's RC Primary School

Books

On a dusty shelf
Books wait to be discovered
Can be tales or facts.

Elizabeth Tyler (8)
St John's RC Primary School

Winter

Sparkling icicles cling on to the gleaming walls
And glittering cobwebs hang on gates.
Snowflakes are trailing down like rocking babies.
The stripped trees are flickering in the breeze.
Howling wolves bark in the pale moonlight.

Michael Brennan (7)
St Mary's RC Primary School

CHRISTMAS

Upon the amber roof, a gold-lit star is out
Reflecting in the animals' drinking trough.
Inside the cold stable,
Animals move in the blackness
Where Mary and Joseph sit down quietly.
There is a noise of a baby crying,
Lying down in the yellow straw by a little candle.
An ox puffs over the baby.
The wind howls outside
In the pitch-black sky.

Joshua Angell (8)
St Mary's RC Primary School

THE SEA

Waves crash like colossal elephants, so rapidly.
The froth on top is like refreshing milk.
Light shines on the water like glittering diamonds.
On calm days the tiny waves steal sand from the shore.
On a stormy day the vast waves crash on the cliffs,
Like a bull butting.

Grace Byron (8)
St Mary's RC Primary School

AUTUMN

Spiky conker shells drop off trees like meteorites,
They shine in the darkness of shady trees.
Scraps of leaves hang on the edges of branches like snake skin,
Acorns fall like rain.

Adam Copus (7)
St Mary's RC Primary School

IN THE STABLE

Above the stable roof,
There is a glittering star in the ebony sky,
Giving the world light.
A damp door hangs from its hinges, creaking open.
Golden straw crackles under my feet,
The animals snore in the chilly silence,
A lantern flickers in the room
And Mary and Joseph huddle together.
King Jesus is crying in the gloomy corner.

Alexander Jacobs (8)
St Mary's RC Primary School

AUTUMN IS COMING

Autumn plodded across the street,
Brushing flaming leaves behind him.
Conkers fell out of his leathery pocket,
His croaky voice scared the animals away.
His beard was spiky with conker shields.

Sam Belizaire (8)
St Mary's RC Primary School

THE STABLE

As I am about to open the stable door,
I look and say, 'How can Christ be born here?'
The door of wobbly wood has ivy growing,
'How can Christ be born here?'

I push open the door to see inside
And it creaks a bit and it creaks some more.
I see Mary and Joseph on the dusty floor.
'How can Christ be born here?'

Mary picks up the baby, the Prince of Peace,
The animals' breath warms Jesus
As they huff and puff away.
'How can Christ be born here?'

I can smell the donkey.
Mary is saying, 'It's just a bit of shelter,'
And baby Jesus is crying.
And now I'll never forget that night
When I saw baby Jesus born here.

Gemma Tugwell (7)
St Mary's RC Primary School

WINTER VISIT

Jack Frost has been
Icicles dangling from his mouth.
He made the windows all frosty,
The pond all icy.
Hailstones drift from his fingers,
He brushes the trees' hair with his clothes
And gobbles up the bushes in snow.
Behind his back is Death.

Keely Noad (7)
St Mary's RC Primary School

JACK FROST

Jack Frost trails snow over torn trees and iced houses.
Sleet ice slips from my shivering hands.
Icicles hang like sharp spears.
Trees sway and creak in the vicious wind.
The pond cracks into stars and spikes.

Rebecca Costello (7)
St Mary's RC Primary School

IN WINTER

Silver mists, dancing, whirling,
Snowflakes fluttering, skipping twirling,
Icicles hanging from bare trees,
Will the winter ever cease?
Glittery pearls that freeze your hands,
Hurling ice that froze the lands,
Shivering children, rosy cheeks,
Behind winter, spring takes a peek.

Christina Bovill-Rose (8)
St Mary's RC Primary School

WINTER NIGHT

Above me in the starlit air,
Snowflakes fall like fading angels.
On the snow-covered trees, the wind tears the branches apart.
The frost started sleeping on the windowpane,
The snow started dozing on the grass.
Icicles were growing fast under the drain,
That's what happened beneath the ebony sky.

Drew Goodchild (8)
St Mary's RC Primary School

FISH

Bubbles coming up
Looking up and down
Rainbow colours flashing
Looking for food
Whizzing fast!

Joseph Scarff (8)
Weston All Saints Primary School

THE MOON

The moon is like a silver ball
Glittering in the sky,
Full of diamonds.
The moon is white as the snow
And it glows,
Gliding through the sky as it blinds all the stars.
The moon is mysterious,
When I look at the moon I see a face.
The moon sparkles and it's bright,
It brightens up the night sky.
Walking through the world,
Getting tired,
Soon it has to go.
I'll see you tomorrow.

Emily Hurford (7)
Weston All Saints Primary School

FOXES

Long, bushy, red tail
Burrowing deep underground
Beneath an old oak.

Cubs playing deep underground
Waiting hungrily for tea.

Flaming red, warm coat
Snapping jaws ready to pounce
Chomping on chicken.

Sucking paws and licking lips
Lying lazily snoozing.

Bethany Walker (9)
Weston All Saints Primary School

JACK THOMAS

Jack Thomas was a lucky lad
Though what happened to him was rather sad

You see, while walking across the road
Always chatting about things like the Morse Code

He would take a long time with his constant pattering
To cross the road, always chattering

The drivers would start to moan and groan
Because they were sick of Jack right down to their bones

Then one day, very tired of Jack
A few of the drivers came together in a pack

They formed a daring, gruesome plan
To get rid of Jack as he came away from his nan's

They hopped in their cars and went their separate ways
One came down Stall Street, and one up Park Glaze

One came down Phin Street, one up Chinch Alley
Revving their engines as if in a rally

They cornered poor Jack and ran him over, I say
But let this be a lesson to you today

Never start blabbing and then not stop
Because you might make some enemies who want to see you go *pop!*

Imogen Tinkler (9)
Weston All Saints Primary School

DAN AND HIS DISGUSTING HABIT

Dan's disgusting habit was chewing plastic.
He thought it was so fantastic.
The piece of plastic was just a speck,
But it got stuck in his neck.

The doctors came and saw his neck,
There was no cure for this big speck.
Now he's dead and blown away,
He does not live on this new day.

Michael Hiscott (9)
Weston All Saints Primary School

MY HOUSE

Hearing my brother's ray guns zapping at unseen aliens,
Hearing the pages of my book fluttering apart,
Hearing my brothers arguing about something,
Hearing my mum cooking our food.

Smelling our cats pooing smellily in their toilet,
Smelling the toilet that's been left unflushed. *Pooh!*
Smelling the warm, comfortable smell of my bed,
Smelling food burn!

Tasting lemonade, fizzy as can be,
Tasting burnt sausages, too hard to eat,
Tasting crunching chick-sticks, cooked by jolly old Mum,
Tasting Sunday chicken, tender as can be.

Seeing spinning dishwasher, cleaning all the dishes,
Seeing kittens tearing round the room,
Seeing computer sending my latest e-mail,
Seeing blazing fire spitting sparks up the chimney.

Touching the family in a humungous hug,
Touching delicately, the keys of the piano,
Touching the silky fur of the cats,
Touching the transparent waters of the bath.

Samuel Taylor (8)
Weston All Saints Primary School

A SENSE POEM

Hearing my dazzling dogs barking their heads off
Hearing my sister sobbing to her friends
Hearing sizzling sausages
Hearing squealing squeaks coming from cute little guinea pigs.

Smelling stinking toilets - poo!
Smelling the fresh, fascinating outdoor flower scent
Smelling lush, lovely pizza waiting for me on the table
Smelling cool water turning into ice
Smelling burning bacon spitting out loud, frying in the pan.

Tasting Cadbury's Caramel chocolate
Tasting delicious dumplings, yummy, yum, yum!
Tasting big baked beans, lovely!
Tasting great grilled chicken, *mmmm!*

Seeing soggy washing hanging on the line
Seeing tiny, tantalising rays of sun through my bedroom window
Seeing continental croissants warm and yummy on my plate
Seeing rapidly rushing spiders crawling up the wall!

Sam White (8)
Weston All Saints Primary School

SENSES AT HOME

Hearing the rumbling rock music in my lovely lounge.
Hearing my dad's peculiar piano playing.
Hearing the sweet singing of Rachel.
Hearing my annoying alarm clock, it's waking me up.

Seeing the fire flickering away.
Seeing my sister doing her history homework on the floor.
Seeing my toys all over our blue, cosy carpet.
Seeing my Shetland sheepdog playing rough and tumble.

Feeling the smooth surface of the wood table.
Feeling the furry feeling of the clothes I'm wearing.
Feeling wet washing ready to be hung outside to dry.
Feeling the softness of a fluffy flannel.

Tasting my dinner, tangy tortillas.
Tasting spicy sausages.
Tasting sweet sherbet for pudding.
Tasting minty mouthwash afterwards.

Juliet Carrick (8)
Weston All Saints Primary School

THE BROKEN CHAIR

There once was a broken chair,
so Alice you'd better beware.

The seat broke and she fell on the floor,
so her bottom went bump and felt so sore.

The next day the back broke off,
so Alice fell and started to cough.

Next, the third day came,
and something like this happened again.

Then one day a leg broke,
so Alice fell and started to choke.

A second later Alice jumped,
and then I heard bump, bump, bump.

Her parents soon started to dread,
but in seconds she was dead!

Joshua White (8)
Weston All Saints Primary School

SENSES AT HOME

Seeing green grass spread all over the garden.
Through the trees I can see traffic.
I look out and I see different coloured birds flying through the blue sky.
I can hear screaming children outside.
I can hear zooming cars going by.
I can hear chirping birds in the trees.
I can hear people banging on the doors.
I can taste my mum's cooking which is delicious.
I love the taste of cola, and how it fizzes up my throat,
But the best taste of all is chocolate!
I can feel the buttons on the controller.
I can feel the wind going by.
I can feel wood on the door.
I can feel the static on the TV.

Alex Bryant (9)
Weston All Saints Primary School

BATHTIME

Splashing in my bath, splash, splash
Bubbles in my bath, bubble, bubble
Relaxing in my bath, *mmmm*
Rubber duck in my bath, quack, quack
Swishing in my bath, swish, swish
And a nice warm *bath!*
A nice soft towel
Wrapping round *me!*
Silky powder just for *me!*

Amy Cousins (7)
Weston All Saints Primary School

MY PONY BUTTONS

Lively and sensitive,
Sometimes muddy,
Sometimes clean.
He's lovely and soft,
He's funny too,
He sticks out his tongue all the time!
He's sometimes naughty,
I can't see him,
All I can see is a lump of mud,
Shaped like a pony I know,
I take him in and dust him off,
Hiding there under the mud
Is a muddy, old pony called Buttons.

Amy Rotheram (8)
Weston All Saints Primary School

PEOPLE PASSING BY

Sipping coffee
On my own in the cafe,
Freezing cold.
People walking
Down the street,
Noisy like a humming bee.
People running
In the rain,
Cars whizzing in and out,
Mum's running
With the buggy.

Maisie Coyle (8)
Weston All Saints Primary School

THE SCARY CASTLE

Going for a walk
In the woods,
Happily as ever,
My bags get heavier and heavier.
Dark and cold,
The moon comes out.
I stopped and I saw a castle,
In I went,
Too scary to stay,
The doors went *slam!*
I slipped and screamed!
Went up the red staircase,
Bang!
Oh no! A Beast!
Stares into my eyes,
Puts me in a dungeon,
Freezing to death!

Natasha Jacobs (8)
Weston All Saints Primary School

FROGS AT NIGHT

Frogs at night
Do not bite
Or give a fright
At night.
They are green
They are noisy
They are very slimy.
Sometimes they are very small
They always splash into a pond.

Tom Folkes (7)
Weston All Saints Primary School

PAINTING

A blob of yellow for the summer.
A stroke of black for the night.
A splash of red for the autumn leaves.
Cover the page with white.
I think I will paint a sign
For Santa, so he knows I am here.
I think I will paint a red, red nose
That will show him the way.
I will put my paints away,
Ready for another day.

Oliver Soar (8)
Weston All Saints Primary School

LEOPARDS

Leopards running
Through the grass,
Pouncing on the animals that pass,
Running as fast as they can,
Hiding behind trees
In the forests.

Spotty and strong,
It's tail flicking,
Roar!

Paolo Hollis (8)
Weston All Saints Primary School

HELEN

The story of Helen who would not go to the toilet.

Helen was a little sweetheart
Whose favourite subject at school was art.
When they stopped she gave a shout,
I really don't want to go out.
Later that night it was time for bed,
Her face started to go red.
She really wanted to go to the loo,
But she was ever so afraid to.
Her mummy said, 'Now please don't cry,
You really, really need to try.'
But Helen was not very sure,
And her head started swelling more and more.
She tried to get the ice pack she saw
But she couldn't get through the bedroom door.
Her face it turned a brilliant red,
There was a big explosion and now she's dead.

Corinne Plank (9)
Weston All Saints Primary School

SENSES AT SCHOOL

I can see chattering children looking at dazzling displays.
I can smell delicious dinners getting ready to be eaten.
I can smell the gungy glue used on my collage.
I can feel the smooth desktop and the furry floor.
I can hear creaking chairs while we do our work.
I can hear talking teachers telling someone off.
I can taste the scrumptious sandwiches from my lunch box.

Sophie Burton (9)
Weston All Saints Primary School

AT MY SCHOOL

Hearing children chattering out loud in assembly,
Chatter, chatter.
Hearing the clock going tick-tock, tick-tock, *loudly.*
Hearing teachers talking to one another in the staff room,
Natter, natter.
Hearing tap water running in the boys' and girls' toilets.

Smelling dinner ladies cooking our lunch in the kitchen.
Smelling the smell of the toilets when we walk into them.
Smelling the fresh air when we go outside.
Smelling the colouring pastels when we are colouring.

Touching my pencil case and pencil with my hand.
Touching my book when I read it, flicking the pages.
Touching my ruler when I want to draw a straight line.
Touching the fresh water when I wash my hands,
Whoosh, whoosh.

Seeing the computer being turned on.
Seeing a blackbird in the sky singing a song.
Seeing food on the table being served.
Seeing children singing songs outside in the playground.

Tasting the air in my mouth.
Tasting my lunch which somebody has made for me.
Tasting puddings in my mouth.
Tasting our drinks,
Slurp, slurp.

Rio Arthur (8)
Weston All Saints Primary School

MY WEDDING DRESS

I had a wedding dress,
Pretty, sparkling and puffing out.
The colour was purple
With flowers all over,
With frills
And a point,
With puffy sleeves,
It's as pretty as a queen.
The next day the bride got married.

Hannah Kennedy (8)
Weston All Saints Primary School